D1517502

Dedication

Parkinson's disease can affect many areas of a person's daily life, but it does not need to become the whole life story. There are countless courageous stories demonstrating the creative and inspirational things that people living with Parkinson's disease accomplish every day. We are pleased to feature these stories from a show of proud hands.

Teva Neuroscience dedicates this photographic book, *"Proud Hands,"* to the approximately 1 million people in the United States living with Parkinson's disease, their dedicated caregivers, families, and committed healthcare providers. We celebrate each and every one of you and your *proud hands*. You are an inspiration to us all.

Acknowledgements

Teva Neuroscience would like to recognize all the people in the United States who are affected by Parkinson's disease, those individuals who contributed so generously to this book, and our many associates who live our vision of being the North American leader in neurology through the quality of our people, the quality of our products, and our focus on the patient.

We also wish to extend our sincere gratitude to the American Parkinson Disease Association (APDA) for their work in sharing the message of and distributing *"Proud Hands." All proceeds from the sale of this book go directly to the APDA to support research, people living with Parkinson's disease, their caregivers, and Parkinson's education.*

Cover: Cover illustration is based on actual photos of hands in the shape of "V" for victory over Parkinson's, a common hand symbol seen by people participating in the annual Parkinson's Unity Walk.

Foreword

When I read the personal stories captured within this book, these windows into the soul in the face of Parkinson's disease, my heart just leaps. These testimonials are so inspiring and remind me of the courage my father embodied during his journey with PD. I have been profoundly shaped by my own father's diagnosis of Parkinson's disease, and, early on, it wasn't easy.

In 1983, I was a college freshman in New York when I noticed a limp in my dad's leg. I said to him, "Hey dad, why are you walking like Fred Sanford?" My dad shot back, "You just focus on getting good grades or you will be runnin' a junk yard like Fred!" As a television writer, my father, Matt Robinson, had written several episodes of the popular '70s sitcom, "Sanford and Son." He was so witty and brilliant, my dad. Having originated the role of "Gordon" on "Sesame Street," and continuing on to become a writer/producer for "The Cosby Show," he had everything to live for. The early '80s were not a great time to get a diagnosis of PD. Of course no time is ideal, but this was before the resource-friendly Internet or the powerful presence of public pillars of courage like Muhammad Ali. I struggled to get any real, helpful information for my young 44-year-old dad and my family. It was just a very dark, hopeless time...

Now, in 2007, it makes me smile to know the 28 courageous people in this book are shining a bright light with their uplifting stories. They will make a difference in the lives of others struggling with PD. Through Parkinson's, they have gained new-found strength and resolve, and they are the solid shoulder that many others have now come to lean upon. A book like this would have been such a useful and uplifting source of hope for our family when my father was diagnosed.

Like so many others across this country who are affected by Parkinson's, both men and women, mothers and sisters, grandfathers and grandsons, they get up every morning and make the choice to beat PD day-by-day. Through their strength, their courage, their humor, their honesty, their unquenchable spirit – they show us daily that their proud hands are raised high for everyone to see and grab hold.

The day my father walked me down the aisle for my wedding in 1995 stands out as a glorious memory of his own unquenchable spirit. Having dealt with PD for a decade already, his body wasn't cooperating with him the week prior to the wedding, and he was so worried he would not make it down the aisle. Not only did he strut his stuff with his chest puffed up, but he twirled and dipped me for our father/daughter dance, then made a brilliant toast that made us laugh and cry!

Inspired by my father's plight, my husband Rodney and I started the HollyRod Foundation 10 years ago to support those with PD and their families. As an actress and professional athlete we had been blessed with the means to financially support my dad until the end. But there are families who find themselves in less fortunate situations. That's where HollyRod comes in. I have been blessed to witness and learn from so many inspiring individuals living with PD. PD shouldn't have the right to diminish anyone's quality of life. It's our mission through the Foundation to ensure it doesn't.

Through this beautiful collection of stories and photos, we see each person's relentless pursuit of sharing a message of hope. Even though they are just a small few banded together by a cause – as one, their voice is loud and strong.

I applaud each of these proud hands, and the millions of others around the world. Their proud hands have touched me, and I hope they will touch you too.

Holly Robinson Peete

I never knew I could paint. When you have Parkinson's disease, the idea of picking up a paintbrush is challenging, but now I paint constantly: landscapes, abstracts, still-life studies, and my favorite, ballerinas. In all, I have completed more than 100 paintings since I began painting in June of 2003 at the age of 44.

My name is Elena Tuero, and for 17 years of my life, I was in a losing battle with a disease that gradually stole my most basic capabilities. But, one summer in June of 2003, my life began again thanks to a surgical procedure. There is no cure for Parkinson's, but the surgery has granted me an interlude to experience the full use of all my blessed faculties.

And so, I continue to paint while my hand remains steady. People say I'm pretty good at it. The critics I try to please, however, are my daughters, Gisselle (26), Tiffany (18), and Vanessa (17), and my beloved mother. When my daughters bring friends to the house, they introduce me with pride telling them, "My mother is an artist." That is all the praise I will ever need to hear.

I don't know how long this will last, or what the future holds for me, but I'm determined to cherish every second of my life, take time to appreciate the beauty of the morning, the shape of clouds, and embrace those I love.

Elena Tuero
Freehold, New Jersey

In July of 2006, we received the news that I had Parkinson's disease. A diagnosis of Parkinson's is always devastating, but especially for an active mother of three. I'm 45 years old with two kids at home, one at college, and a teaching career to manage. It was devastating news because there were so many activities I enjoyed that involved using my hands. I grieved for the time when I would not be able to use my hands to sign, paint, play the piano, garden, exercise, and many other activities that involved using my hands.

I was determined to continue the activities I loved despite my PD. I immediately cut back on stress, changed my eating patterns, and began exercising. The activities that I have always enjoyed are still a part of my life. They may take me a little longer and take more effort, but continuing the activities that I love makes me feel alive and more determined to fight the symptoms of this disease.

I hold a degree in deaf education (Texas Tech, '83 cum laude), and interpret for the deaf at our church. I have taught for more than 16 years, serving multi-handicapped children, pre-school and, most recently, kindergarten. Before beginning my medication and exercise regimen last year, I could not interpret more than a few minutes before my hands would tire. Last week, I interpreted the entire hour.

I no longer teach kindergarten full-time because of the stress, but I am still able to enjoy working with the children by serving as a teacher's aide in first grade. I just finished painting my son's house. I rode tandem with my husband for 22 miles, a feat I had not even attempted before my diagnosis. I am in better physical condition than many of my friends. Who knows what the future holds, but I am making the most of the present.

Lori McWilliams
Allen, Texas

In 1984, at the age of 56, I was diagnosed with Parkinson's disease. I retired from teaching elementary school science in 1986. I presently work for our park district as a volunteer. I collect and transplant perennial plants and shrubs from old farm sites being torn down to construct new houses or businesses in our community. I also have written two books, "Osmis, the Cursed Egyptian Maiden," and " Short, Shorter, and Shorter Stories." The latter was a finalist for "Book of the Year" in 2006. I am working on my third book. I also paint landscapes and animals with acrylics and make clay animal sculptures.

I like to create ornaments or centerpieces constructed from paper doilies. They are numbered as my work has progressed. By removing material in between the original design, I open the spaces between, giving a lacy appearance. I fold and glue the doilies together, to form a "snow flake." I have just finished assembling several snowflakes on thin metal rods, tied together with fishing line, to make mobiles. These will hang in local libraries to advertise fall classes where I show people how to make these beautiful objects.

I also attend monthly writers' group meetings, have enrolled in a community college art class for this fall, and work out at our local health club.

Chuck McCann
Round Lake Beach, Illinois

My passion is watercolor painting; my battle is with Parkinson's disease. I have loved art ever since I opened my first box of crayons and am still inspired by the beauty of color. I am right handed and, fortunately it's my left hand that is most affected by PD. Going through life with a paintbrush in hand has been a wonderful adventure and, although I can no longer work into the late hours like I used to, I still have a lot of watercolor paint and paper that I plan to bring together.

Growing up during the Depression era we had few toys and were forced to use our imaginations in play. So my brother and I made up stories and illustrated them. He grew up to be a writer, and I became an artist. After raising three children, I was able to pursue painting more seriously, showing in galleries, solo and combined exhibits, and winning awards. I also experienced the joy of taking painting excursions to Greece, Switzerland, St. Croix, Virgin Islands, Canada, and across the United States.

Parkinson's disease seems to run in my family. My grandfather had it, my brother has been afflicted with it for approximately 15 years, my deceased brother had Progressive Supranuclear Palsy, and I was diagnosed with "garden variety" PD a couple of years ago after trying for over a year to obtain an accurate diagnosis. My primary concern was how long I would be able to paint.

So far the inspiration and ability still flow, and I hope to be a producing artist for a long time to come. I know that my hands are in God's hands.

Marilyn Ferch
Mundelein, Illinois

As a teacher for 33 years, I always encouraged my students to achieve beyond their own expectations. After being diagnosed with Parkinson's disease, it was now time for me to practice what I had always preached.

My name is Lou DeCaro, and I was diagnosed with PD on July 19th, 2002. My first two years with the disease were some of the darkest but, one morning in December of 2004, I found myself wondering what the rest of my life would look like. The answer was really simple. I had to somehow find the strength to make the best of things and live my life to the fullest.

The first thing I did was decorate the outside of the house for the holidays. This was followed by a series of home improvement projects that included painting several rooms, installing shelves and molding, and remodeling my kitchen. With the help of friends, my house, and my outlook, continued to change as the year came to an end. Before I knew it spring had arrived, and I started to plant flowers. I also began oil painting and decided to do volunteer work for the American Parkinson Disease Association (APDA).

Today, I'm vice president of the Long Island chapter of the APDA. I try to stay as active as I can, but some days my body won't allow it. That might be something I may never have control over again, but my attitude is another matter altogether. I have learned that having the right attitude, and a lot of faith, makes almost anything possible.

Lou DeCaro
Wading River, New York

I am a perennial student. I went to college for nine years and earned a bachelor of arts degree, teaching credential, and a master's of library science from the University of California, Berkeley, and a law degree from Hastings Law School. I taught legal writing and research at Boalt Law School and had a long, rewarding career as an elementary school librarian. I have been married to my husband, Julian, for 48 years, and we have two married daughters and three grandsons, ages 2, 6, and 9. I was diagnosed with Parkinson's disease five years ago.

I always have enjoyed sewing and doing all kinds of crafts. I have made many things for our home including placemats, napkins, tablecloths, pillows, window coverings, slipcovers, upholstery, bedspreads, dust ruffles, quilts, and more.

I also make clothing and handbags for myself. I am fascinated with textiles, and have collected fabrics from all over the world such as Thailand, West Africa, and Japan. My husband says I have enough fabric to open a fabric store. I also like to knit.

Lately, I have made many scarves inspired by the new and exciting yarns that are now available. I also make jewelry using purchased beads or making my own beads with polymer clay. I design note cards using photographs my husband has taken. I donate sets of these to the gift shop at our local hospital. I get much satisfaction from giving gifts that I have designed and created myself.

Even though I have a pretty bad tremor in my right hand, I feel lucky that I have been able to continue doing the activities that bring me so much pleasure. It is a mysterious, but fortunate, phenomenon that when I am involved doing this kind of intricate craft work, my tremor seems to disappear.

Sue Lifschiz
San Rafael, California

I retired to Florida, after a career in high school health, physical education, and athletics, hoping for much-needed rest and relaxation. After being diagnosed with Parkinson's disease, I knew my retirement years would be full of new and unfamiliar physical challenges. I wanted to capitalize on my experiences as a coach and create my own Parkinson's disease-specific exercise plan, not only to help myself stay strong and manage my symptoms, but also to help others.

My name is Bill Hillman, and I have been living with PD since 1997. I believe that exercise is one of the best tools to use to deal with, and control, Parkinson's. I have arrested some of my symptoms and have also been able to keep my Parkinson's under control. My exercise program has improved my range of motion, built strength, and reduced stress. I've created some exercise videos for people living with PD, and I enjoy sharing them with people from all over the country.

To follow my exercise program you don't have to purchase any equipment, rather you just use items that most people commonly have around the house. For example, to work on my grip and expand my coordination, I squeeze, juggle, and bounce tennis balls, softballs, and handballs. I also use small stones from my garden in my exercise routine. I keep them in a Tupperware container. I first empty it out, and then pick the stones up, one by one, and put them back in the container. Using a margarine container filled with different sizes of buttons, I dump them out and then put them back into the container through a slit on the top. These exercises don't require a lot of energy or strength, but they help with coordination.

I want people with PD to know that they can improve. Just stick with it, because exercise will make a difference!

Bill Hillman
Sun City Center, Florida

My accordion has befriended me through the past 11 years of living with Parkinson's disease. We became buddies just around the time of my diagnosis in 1996. The day before I was diagnosed with PD, I almost heaved her across the room out of frustration. I struggled to play her with my slow moving, shaky fingers. During my honeymoon stage with PD, I earned 29 trophies for solo accordion performances in Denver — first, second, and third place trophies, some as tall as 20 inches. I performed in accordion concerts at Los Arcos in Puerto Vallarta, Mexico, the San Diego Zoo, Disneyland in Anaheim, the Space Needle in Seattle, the Parliament Building in Victoria, and at Stanley Park in Vancouver, British Columbia.

I squeezed with the accordion ensemble "Silver Notes," as we delighted audiences in assisted living and nursing home facilities with our music. With the progression of PD, I struggled to hold, and carry, the 30-pound instrument and open and close the bellows. I purchased a 13-pound electronic accordion without bellows. When I played a big band medley on my new accordion, I sounded like a one-woman Glenn Miller orchestra. With the honeymoon stage of my PD behind me, my neurologist referred me for brain surgery. I overheard her say, "Kate needs to continue playing her accordion." I even had my favorite accordion CDs soothing me during surgery.

I recently discovered that I was one of two living accordionists in the world with PD and was delighted to track down Charlie Nimovitz, the other living accordion player with PD. My accordion has helped me forget about having PD and has allowed me to spread the joy of my music to others. She is a faithful friend.

Kate Kelsall
Northglenn, Colorado

My body has Parkinson's. I don't. It doesn't define me and it only limits my life in that narrow corridor that I've set for myself between full-blown activity and caution. My life, and this disease, is in my hands. My goal is to stay vigorous. Before getting out of bed, I begin each morning with stretches and rotations. My body is now ready to greet the day. Daily physical exercise has become my mantra. Weight training, pool aerobics at the gym, treadmill walking, or Tai Chi — each one serves me well. With each stride on the treadmill, I visualize dopamine flowing into my brain. With every Tai Chi movement, my focus is balance and harmony.

Since I can no longer knit (you need 10 dexterous fingers), I crochet (only six are necessary). My granddaughters love their ponchos with any of grandma's stitches. Ten years ago, I began reading to first and second graders in a local school. Though I now walk slower to each class, reading aloud gives me the opportunity to project my voice and practice my breathing. The enthusiastic response of 6 and 7 year olds spurs me forward again.

For renewal, I write poetry.

Finding gratification in each day nourishes my perspective and enthusiasm for life. Parkinson's disease does not define me. I am the same ebullient, involved person that I was at 68, four years ago when I was first diagnosed. My leg may tremor and drag, but it doesn't stop me from daily activity. I just don't skip anymore.

Joan Wolstein
Calabasas, California

I have been a sculptor for at least 35 years. In the beginning, my work included bronze figurative sculptures, particularly dancers. I have continued to work despite being diagnosed with Parkinson's disease 17 years ago.

However, as my dexterity became more and more compromised, the details needed for figurative work became harder to achieve, and I began doing abstract sculptures instead. My media expanded to metal, wood, and, especially, found objects. Continuing to sculpt has been my lifeline. In addition to sculpting, I enjoy water sports like canoeing, kayaking, and sailing.

With the help of college students I hired as assistants, I have been able to keep working and am excited to be mentoring young artists. A win-win situation!

Jack Holme
Darien, Illinois

My name is Marie Oben, and I was diagnosed with Parkinson's disease when I was 44 years old.

I have active hands even though I have PD. I have worked as a first grade teacher for 24 years now and am a mother of two children. I love to garden, fish, teach, bake and, most of all, take care of my family. Because my children have Ehlers-Danlos Syndrome, they couldn't attend summer camp. My daughter asked me to do something with her because she was bored. I decided to show her how to make my favorite brownie recipe. Once she made her first batch of brownies, she said she wanted to sell them. I called a friend who owns an office supply store and asked her if she could sell them. My friend, who cared very much for my children and loved my brownie recipe, told me to bring the brownies to her store. That's how we started our baking business.

Then, little by little, and day by day, we have been adding old family recipes to our home-based business, and my daughter has been learning, and using, her creative abilities. It's a family affair as my son helps deliver the desserts, and my husband pampers my daughter by buying her new stuff to cook with in our kitchen.

Right now we sell around 20 different kinds of desserts, and, every summer, we add a new dessert recipe. Our best selling sweets are tres leches, carrot cake, coffee custard, brownies, Sidney cake, chocolate cake, and the classic wedding cake with pastiage.

My daughter will be graduating from the university in three years, and our family goal is to open a fine bakery for everyone to enjoy our desserts just as much as we love to bake and eat them.

Marie Oben
Guayama, Puerto Rico

I had been practicing yoga for over 20 years, and teaching it for 16. So, although I was almost 70 years old, it was a great shock the day I suddenly couldn't do a handstand. It was even more of a shock to be diagnosed with Parkinson's. My immediate response was to increase my yoga practice. In addition, my wife began giving me frequent Jin Shin Jyutsu treatments to release blockages to the energy flow in my body.

My neurologist was amazed when, six months later, I was tremendously improved and still able to stay off medication despite having all the primary symptoms, and most of the secondary, as well. With the addition of medication a few months later, I lost the stiffness in my shoulders and neck, and I got back the handstand — and an even more difficult backbend. I also regained use of my arm swing, turns, and a normal walk.

This inspired my wife and me to create a program for others with Parkinson's to maintain and improve their flexibility, strength, and balance! People usually think yoga is difficult but, in the past several years, I have focused on adjusting poses to enable older persons who have many physical restrictions to gain function in accordance with their own capacities, and have fun, too.

We now combine our own experience with that of other practitioners of both yoga and Jin Shin Jyutsu in a two-on-one treatment session for an affordable fee. We also like to include the spouses and other caretakers who certainly need the same level of support!

Paul Zeiger
Denver, Colorado

I've had Parkinson's disease for 16 years since age 35. I'm now 51 years old. Needless to say, I'm a "young on-setter."

I've had my horse, Rusty, for about 12 years. I bought Rusty about four years before I was diagnosed with PD. As my disease progressed, Rusty adjusted his movement to my increasing inability to move. I'm sure you have all read that animals "know" when a person is sick and weak, well Rusty always has been very careful and patient with me during the PD "freezing" times.

When I ride Rusty, he takes slow and deliberate steps and is totally in tune with the rigidity in my body. On the other hand, when my husband rides Rusty he's a normal, spunky horse. Sometimes, when I'm leading Rusty to his stall for his evening meal, my body freezes and Rusty waits patiently until I can walk again. There aren't too many horses that will wait for you to move when their evening meal is in sight. I truly believe that my regular horseback riding has helped me to keep going, both mentally and physically. When I'm galloping Rusty though a meadow or field, my body feels normal and free as if I do not have PD. It is truly a wonderful feeling.

Sandy, our dog of mixed healer/lab lineage, has been with us for over 13 years. Sandy is a loyal, unconditionally loving, devoted dog, and she loves Rusty. Like my horse, Sandy "knows" that I have a disease, and she is always by my side whether I'm waiting for my PD pills to "kick in" or running alongside of Rusty. Sandy has been a kindred and loving companion through my journey with PD. Dogs and horses are wonderful creatures and true friends, and I'm thankful for my friends.

Pam Gehrts
Granite Bay, California

Who would have ever believed the words, "you have Parkinson's disease at the age of 33." I sure didn't want to. I had a brand new baby at home, a good job, and my independence.

I am here to tell you, though, it is going to be okay. Yes, it took me some time to come to the realization that I have a disease that will, in time, change some aspects of my life. The key to accepting that, was finding I have other talents and new avenues to walk down.

Having PD has brought out my creative side. I have found I really enjoy writing poems. Photography is also a fun hobby I have more time for now. My true passion, though, is being a mom to my 5-year-old daughter. She keeps me on my toes at all times, helps me stay active, and gives me a desire to keep pushing forward. She puts a fire in my heart to kick PD. At night's end, tired and worn, I tuck her into bed and thank God for sharing her with me. The unconditional love of a child is truly priceless.

My victory each day is being able to wrap my arms around her and kiss her goodnight. As her tiny fingers grasp mine, I can ease all her fears and give her comfort that I am here for her. At the same time, she is completing me as well. I do not question why I have PD. I accept it, move forward, and gain strength from it.

Find that inner place that brings you peace and puts a smile in your heart and on your face, then embrace and enjoy it. You deserve to be happy. Nothing can stand in your way and keep you down, except you.

Kelly Maurer
Perrysburg, Ohio

My name is Charles Barasch, and I was diagnosed with Parkinson's disease in 1993 at the age of 42. Although my symptoms have steadily progressed since I was diagnosed, I think continuing to exercise and staying active has kept them from progressing as rapidly as they otherwise would have. I never rollerbladed before I was diagnosed with PD, now I rollerblade a lot:

"Rollerblading on L-dopa"
Once it kicks in, my arms
swing in time to the hips' sway
and with the wind at my back,
a smooth stretch of blacktop,
I pirouette in my mind
like Charlie Chaplin
in "Modern Times," defying
the forces of physics
and aging, accelerate
out of the cul-de-sac
with reckless crossovers
and, turning home
before meds wear off,
relax, lean forward,
hands on thighs and like
derby queen Joan Weston
after a jam, remove
my helmet, shake out
luxurious bleached tresses.

Charles Barasch
Plainfield, Vermont

My first personal experience with Parkinson's disease was 13 years ago as a caregiver of my mother, a brave and courageous woman who fought the battle of PD as long as she could. In her memory, I'm writing this story of how she taught me courage, strength, prayer, and faith in God. Also, she taught me to never give up because there is always hope!

In her memory, I help support others to learn more about PD and encourage them. I am honored to walk on this journey with each and every person that I meet with PD.

I am also a home health nurse and see patients with PD in their homes. I teach them about PD, their medications, and see that their medical needs are met. I am also a firm believer in the touch of healing hands and prayer. With faith, prayer, and God, the journey is much easier. So many times we forget the spiritual side of healing. I have learned from my mother's faith, and my own. I have also found through spending time with my patients in their homes that praying together also gives them the strength and encouragement to succeed in their journey with PD.

I have seen prayer do more than any other treatment. "By His stripes we are Healed" Isaiah 53:5.

Patty Salmon
Valley View, Texas

I believe my commitment to high-intensity exercise is mitigating the potential symptoms of Parkinson's disease. My competition times for sprint triathlons continue to improve. My next endeavor is the Virginia Senior Olympics, then on to the National Senior Olympics. I challenge other people with Parkinson's to join me!

"Run, Bike, Swim to Win"

I've always been an athlete of sorts

Run, swim, and bike are my sports.

When Parkinson's hit,

I couldn't just sit

Like a rusty old ship docked at port.

I first took an exercise class

I had to do something fast.

Fitness set me in motion,

Like some magic potion

To put my PD in the past.

Cheryl Majeske
Quinton, Virginia

My name is Ann Marie Konopka. Most people know me as Annie, and I was diagnosed with young onset Parkinson's disease in February 2004.

My world was turned upside down. I found myself becoming agitated very quickly, and my stress level was beyond the norm. I felt horrible inside and out. I got tired of feeling so bad and decided it was time to get on with my life.

So, in May 2005, I started an online support group called "USA PD PALS" *(www.usapdpals.com)* with my friend, Judy Hensley. Then, in April 2005, I and several of my family and friends, walked in the "Unity Walk" in Central Park. In 2006, we raised more than $17,000 for the Parkinson's Unity Walk community.

I have a very strong desire to continue learning and telling my stories to others. Last summer, I self-published my first children's book, "The Tale of a Parkie Princess." My hope for this book is to give parents a tool that will allow them to explain the affects that Parkinson's disease may have on their loved ones. My friend, Judy, and I also collaborated with six PD patients to publish a book called "Stories from the Heart: Our Parkie Lives." This book reflects the lessons learned from having the disease. I'm choosing to use my disease in a positive way by creating awareness, and promoting education and fundraising for research.

In early 2007, I decided to take a chance by entering the "Mrs. New Jersey USA" pageant. I was honored to be the recipient of the "People's Choice Award" and first runner-up for the "Community Service Award."

Ann Konopka
Kendall Park, New Jersey

I close my eyes, try to make it go away. Benji is ill. No "magic" doggie pill. He's in the hospital, very weak. To touch his belly, he yelps in pain and fear. I muffle my words, "Please don't hurt my Benji dear!" More tests will give us the answer. The doctors think it is cancer.

A decade ago, this fluffy white pup, we bonded quickly when I first picked him up. As time slips by and my PD gets worse, I hide my pain in photography and verse. I rely more each day on Benji's devotion, helping to distract me from my loss of locomotion.

Laboring climbing stairs, taking my time, Benji waits, eyes reassuring me, "You're doing just fine!" Each morning he peeks to see if I'm awake. So smart, he knows my closed eyes are fake. After checking some more, then gently pawing my arm, I know I've got to get up he's my early alarm.

Now, it's three in the morning. I'm alone in my bed. He's in a cage, towel under his head, I.V. in his paw, all alone, too. There oughta be a law!

Lying there, I whisper in the night air, "Is anyone listening?" Benji, my dearest friend, my "bud" for ten years, is missing. We planned to grow old, side by side. "Don't leave me, pal, I need you on this ride!"

Finally, the pathologist's report: The margins are clear. This life will not yet abort. Now we know to attack it head-on was oh so right. Thank you for Benji's chance to fight.

As nature heals my dear friend, the future awaits. Our joy will not end. Now, with each breath comes a happy sigh, "We made it pal. I think we can fly!"

Sherri Wolf
San Diego, California

It is the waking moment of the day that I struggle to reach out to my toes and fingers. With a breath, I softly begin to move my hands that have been frozen in place throughout the night. Using the practice of centering, I rest with the thought that I will begin another day within a moment. Again I reach out to my toes, moving to my feet, ankles, knees, hips, to rest with my back. As I take another breath, I feel my lungs expand, and my rib cage complains of the stretch.

My shoulders move naturally with the movement, but not without me shifting off my pillow. Because of my practice with yoga, I understand the need to stretch this way. I command my arms to move to a place over my head and again breathe. My day begins.

As the coordinator of the Information and Referral Center for the American Parkinson Disease Association in Iowa, I have learned from many others to take a moment and treasure it. When handing out information to individuals in a support group, or returning an e-mail to someone needing guidance, I remind myself to stand up and move. It becomes more difficult to listen to the reminder, but because of my involvement with others who have also been diagnosed with Parkinson's disease, I continue to push myself. I understand that it is the moments of working in my garden, knitting prayer shawls, and doodling (as I would call it) that helps me.

It is a hand that we use to introduce ourselves, to bring ourselves into a room, to respond to a telephone call, to return an e-mail, to share an understanding, and to say farewell. It is a simple thing, a touch.

Sam Erwin
Des Moines, Iowa

Just because I have Parkinson's disease doesn't mean my life has to slow down one bit. As a matter of fact, since I was diagnosed with PD in 2003, I believe my life has been busier than ever.

My name is Ralph Sliwa, and I was diagnosed with PD at the age of 46. Since then, I don't feel like I've wasted one minute — traveling across the country, meeting others with PD, and talking to people who can help influence the fight for a cure.

It wasn't always that way for me, though. When I went to my first support group meeting, I thought, "what am I doing here?" I felt like I didn't belong. I later realized that not only could they help me, but I also learned to help them through encouragement. I learned there are many others out there dealing with the same thing.

When I turned 50 last year, my friends encouraged me to have a party. I didn't want to, but I realized there might be an opportunity to bring people together for a cure. I asked guests to forego gifts in lieu of a donation to the Michael J. Fox Foundation. We raised more than $14,000 for the foundation at the party, and I was able to donate $500 more to the American Parkinson Disease Association. I actually got to meet Michael J. Fox, and it was one of the most memorable moments of my life.

I'm hoping to continue the tradition again this year. I want to help find a cure for this and help others. The best way for me to do that is to continue to support the organizations that hopefully will one day find a cure.

Ralph Sliwa
Norridge, Illinois

When I was diagnosed with Parkinson's disease in 2002, I was, of course, very upset, but not surprised. My first reaction was, "I need to cram everything into my life now while I still can." I wanted to visit places that I have always dreamed of visiting, revisit places that held precious memories, and get my house in order. I have heard other PD friends say that they also feel driven to do it all.

I have a passion for sewing. I want to make as many keepsake items for friends and family before the time comes that I can no longer thread a needle. This means I am in my sewing room every day for many happy, productive hours.

On December 1, 2006, I quit my job as a receptionist because of stress and fatigue. Since then, I have made quilts, wall hangings, plus lots of other gifts. I have also been able to take vacations with my husband to places like Yellowstone and Niagara Falls. On these trips, I have enjoyed the art of photography. I love taking pictures, and I recently took a short class on the use of cameras, and have learned how to take even better pictures.

I will continue to sew, take pictures, and spend quality time with my family for as long as possible. I am more conscious than ever of taking good care of myself by walking two miles nearly every day, and trying to eat healthy.

Lois Cole
Des Moines, Iowa

I have accomplished more new and unusual things in my life since I've had Parkinson's disease. When I was diagnosed in November 2002, I made some decisions and learned some things about PD that have helped me cope with my illness.

In 2004, I met a lady who has become a great friend and mentor, Peggy Willocks. She has lived with PD for 12 years and is determined to find a cure. Since I met her, I have been active in a local young-onset support group. I have also found support in numerous friends online through PD Web sites. I actually got to meet some of these special people in Savannah, Georgia, at "Parkinson's in the Park." So many of my PD friends give me hope. They inspire me when I talk to them, and I learn how they cope with PD.

In 2006, I promoted PD Awareness month in my city and was interviewed on radio, television and in the newspapers. I also went to New York City, for the first time, for the Parkinson's Unity Walk. Our team raised over $17,000. The hope for a cure is my focus, so I want to do my part to help find a cure.

I bought a book of poems by Tamra Cantore, a young mother with PD, that has been a great source of comfort. I would like to share the last lines in her poem "We are Not Alone": "It's when we're at our weakest, God's mighty strengths revealed, His light guides us through our darkest hour, and in His love we're healed."

Always hold on to hope. Reach out to others and make a difference in their lives and yours. You will make it through and see that there are blessings you can still experience whether you are living with PD or not!

Judy Hensley
Johnson City, Tennessee

My name is Fern Jaffee, and I live in Chicago, Illinois. I was diagnosed with Parkinson's disease when I was 65 years old. Now that I'm 82, I've lived with PD for 17 years.

I guess I am lucky! I cannot keep my hands off things. First, it was toys, then dolls, then came homework. After high school, I went to study optometry, mostly to help children, where I learned how to set machines to measure the distance between eyes, and to stimulate the macula (near the center of the retina of the eye).

When I retired, I took up knitting as my next interest but something went wrong with my stitches. It became impossible to continue. PD started to rear its ugly head. Fortunately, I came across my grandmother's crystal necklace, which she had given me. It needed to be updated. Thank goodness! I found myself immersed in beads and love it to this day.

Fern Jaffee
Chicago, Illinois

One of the positive aspects of Parkinson's disease is that mental thinking powers do not appear to deteriorate. Eight years ago, the neurologist told me I had "garden variety" Parkinson's. I assume he meant that it was a common form, which would be reasonably treatable and, if cared for, I could have a productive life. That is what has happened.

I am still able to tutor, sew, cook, garden, drive, use the computer, and do almost everything I want to do. There are "wearing off" times in the day when my physical body does not function as well. Resting awhile, and sometimes taking a little medication, restores my ability to function.

I live with a grandson and his wife and do the grocery shopping and cooking. I retired from teaching just two years ago. My math skills are still intact, so I can tutor. Sewing for grandchildren or making quilts keeps me active. The Lord has provided many blessings. Life is good.

Barbara Jordan
Overland Park, Kansas

My name is Henry (Hank) Barnett, and I was diagnosed with Parkinson's disease approximately 12 years ago. It started with tremors in the right hand and has progressed since then.

At first, depression set in as I was only in my mid-50s and not yet retired. When I retired at the age of 61, I knew I needed things to do. Of course, I was already a member of the Staten Island Parkinson's Support Group. I decided to go back to bowling, which I had not done for many years. I started Monday mornings with the "Golden Oldies" and met many friendly and helpful seniors. Then I was asked to join some of them Tuesday mornings to bowl again. Once my wife retired, she also started bowling with me Mondays. Now we both bowl Friday afternoons with another couple after having lunch with them.

I also belong to a local AARP chapter and go on many day trips with them. Our bowling league also has dinners and day trips in which we participate. I decided that Parkinson's disease was not going to get to me. For exercise, I wash our two cars and wax them two times a year, but I refuse to help with the house cleaning, ha ha! (Well, sometimes I will do a little vacuuming.)

We enjoy going to Atlantic City a few times a year and, if the weather permits, we walk the Boardwalk. Of course, I do enjoy some gambling, too! I have even learned a little bit about the computer and, if I have trouble sleeping, I play solitaire until I get sleepy.

I have five grandchildren and really enjoy doing things with them. Our 3-year-old granddaughter, Alex, loves to go bowling with me. Bowling is my favorite hobby!

Henry Barnett
Staten Island, New York

When I was diagnosed with Parkinson's disease in June of 2000, it was like a great weight was lifted off my shoulders. It took 18 months, but once diagnosed, I sat down, took a look at my life, and decided I wanted to work on the quality of my life.

The decision to retire took some time, but once decided I went head long into doing all the things I wanted to do. In October 2003, I left the firm where I had worked for 43 years. Since that day, I have been knitting and crocheting afghans, sweaters, hats, stuffed toys — you name it. I discovered floral arranging, gardening, and tried my hands at numerous crafty projects. I also found the benefits of Tai Chi, aerobics, and stretch classes, as well. In fact, last year I participated in the Senior Olympics with my Tai Chi class and demonstrated the various poses. I have been invited back again.

I discovered the American Parkinson Disease Association, Salvatore and Elena Esposito Information & Referral Center's support group for Parkinson's patients and their caregivers. I donate my time assisting the nurse/coordinator and help to create further awareness of Parkinson's by attending health fairs, decorating bulletin boards, as well as volunteering at APDA. I'm having the time of my life despite the Parkinson's — or is it because of Parkinson's disease?

Susan Ernst
Staten Island, New York

Whether I am handing him a treat or hooking on his leash, my dog, Calvin, has brought me such joy on my Parkinson's journey. Every day we walk a mile around our neighborhood.

Some days I may tilt a little to the left and some days I may have more of a shuffle in my step, but Calvin and I never fail to greet those we see on our daily outings. We give friendly waves to the FedEx delivery guys, quote scripture with the postman, and enjoy visits with the wait staff at The White House Restaurant. Of course, Calvin lets folks know that he's protecting me. But, we always enjoy our walks together.

My wife Sherry and I adopted Calvin from Atlanta Pet Rescue two years ago. I'm fond of saying, "No dog has ever loved me like Calvin does!" I am a retired Presbyterian minister and when we asked the name of this funny little dog at the animal shelter they replied, "Calvin." As good Presbyterians and followers of John Calvin, we just knew this puppy was predestined to be our pet!

Donn Wright
Atlanta, Georgia